Volume 2

Presented by
STAN LEE

Edited by Don Daley and Pat Redding.

The 'Nam Trade Paperback
Published by Marvel Comics,
a New World Pictures Company.
387 Park Avenue South, New York,
New York 10016

Manufactured in the United States of America

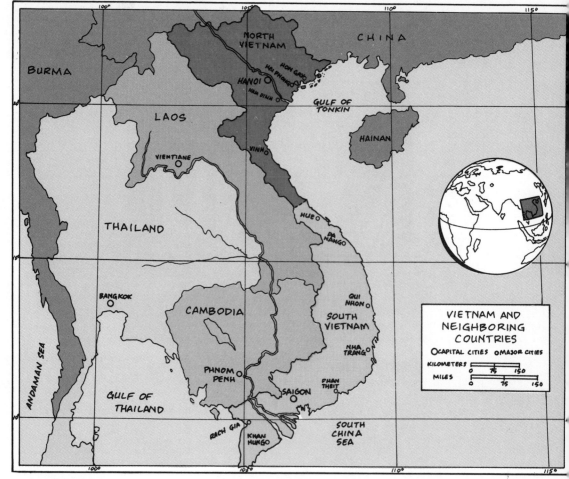

VIETNAM AND
NEIGHBORING
COUNTRIES

○ CAPITAL CITIES   ○ MAJOR CITIES

I've been to Washington D.C. a few times in the last year. Every time I go, I make a trip to the Wall. You all know what the Wall is — it's the Vietnam Memorial, just a short distance from the Lincoln Memorial. I walk along the Wall and look at all the names, more and more every year. All the men who died in Vietnam (or as a result of wounds received there).

Eventually, I reach the portion of the Wall that represents the time I spent there myself. I find a couple of names I recognize, and I spend a few minutes meditating and paying my respects to those contemporaries of mine (some of them buddies) that didn't make it.

It's a solemn and touching place, and everyone that goes there is moved. There's really nothing else like it anywhere in the U.S.

The very existence of the Wall is proof that we're finally ready to accept the reality of the Vietnam War. For too many years, we've tried to force our heads into the sand and pretend the whole thing never happened. That's over. Most Americans are now willing to talk about the war — watch movies about it — read books about it.

That's where THE 'NAM comes in.

Just a couple of years ago, a comic book about the Vietnam War would have been a bad joke. Nobody would have read it — indeed, nobody would have even *thought about doing it.*

But this is now, the Wall is up in our nation's capital, and people are finally willing to learn about the terrible years of the Vietnam War.

I find myself in an odd position. I was trained as a teacher, but I've never really taught. I've always written, in some fashion, and suddenly I find myself teaching a whole new generation of kids about the most costly, most demoralizing War in the history of the United States, the Vietnam War. It's a great responsibility. And a great honor.

In the pages of this book you'll find reproduced issues five through eight of THE 'NAM. An earlier edition spotlighted issues one through four. Hopefully, there'll be other editions to come.

THE 'NAM was designed as a way to present a representative history of the Vietnam War in comic book form. A way to show what the war was like, how it changed people, how it was viewed by the soldier in the field.

It is told in a real-time format. For those who haven't seen the actual comic, that means that the four stories presented here represent a four month period of time from May 1966 to August 1966. Each story is carefully researched to make it as true to reality as is possible in the comic medium. And each story has a point-of-view. This means that we are seeing the stories through the eyes of the characters involved. In this case, through the eyes of one Ed Marks, a young man of 19 who is just into his Tour of Duty in Vietnam.

Even in the four stories presented, we can see Marks changing, from a callow, confused youth into a more aware, more know-

ledgeable man. Like all participants in Vietnam, Marks will come home changed, a different person from what he was when he left. It is through Marks that we see the effect of war on the young men of America — some of whom have never adjusted to the experience.

One of the stories, "The Good Old Days," is my attempt to give the reader a quick primer course in the roots of war, to try to show that the Viet Cong and North Vietnamese are not just nameless, godless enemies. Rather, they are people just like us, people who have been fighting invaders throughout their history, people just trying to have the ability to choose their own destiny.

All in all, working on THE 'NAM has been a learning experience for me as well. An opportunity for me to re-examine my own prejudices, my own hidden devils, my own feelings about the war that changed me just as surely as it changed all the others who were there.

So read on, learn what little I can teach about the Vietnam War. Hopefully, it will inspire some of you to learn more. Perhaps it will help some other veterans rid themselves of their own demons. Whatever it does, whatever it teaches, I hope it adds something to you and your world view. If it does, I will have done my job.

If it doesn't, then it is quite likely that someday some of you may have a Wall of your own to visit, and names to recognize and mourn over. Let's hope that never comes to be.

**DOUG MURRAY
NOVEMBER 1987**

As with any other profession, soldiers have their own private language — a jargon that only seems to make sense to other soldiers. To make things more realistic in THE 'NAM, we will use this jargon wherever possible (some of it is unprintable). Keep in mind that the initial major troop influxes into the 'Nam in 1965–66 were veterans from Japan and Korean stations, thus much of the slang is of Japanese and Korean origin. As time passed, Vietnamese words were picked up and added.

To avoid interfering with the flow of the stories, we have collected the slang terms here, in the glossary, to allow you to check back (or forward) and understand exactly what is being said. We try to be as complete and comprehensive as possible:

101st AIRBORNE DIVISION

25th INFANTRY DIVISION

ASAP: As soon as possible. Right away.

BAMBOO SNAKE: A small, deadly viper indigenous to Southeast Asia.

BOONIES: The bush, the countryside. The untamed, dangerous part of the country outside American bases and cities.

BUCK SERGEANT: A three-striper, the lowest rank of sergeant. Pay grade: E-5.

CHARLIE: Charles, Victor Charlie, the VC. From our point of view, the bad guy, the enemy.

CLERK-TYPIST: The army has a name for everything and verybody. A Clerk-Typist is a trooper whose function is to act as a secretary for the company — of course, the army would *never* use the term secretary (not macho enough by a long shot).

DET CORD: Explosive primer cord. Generally used to prime bangalore torpedoes and other things that go boom. Troops also used them to chop down trees and clear brush — handier and faster than an axe, and easier to carry.

DIDI MOW (or MAU): Vietnamese for "get out quick." Run away.

DIENBIENPHU: A little village near the Laotian border where the last French Fighting Force was defeated in 1954, effectively freeing Vietnam from French rule.

DIKE: The raised earthen area holding water in the rice paddies.

EVAC: Short for evacuation. Special choppers used to pull out wounded, dead, and groups in serious trouble.

EXTRACTION: Using a helicopter to pull troops out of the bush. Usually done fast and dirty, the chopper only hitting the ground for a few seconds.

FIRST SERGEANT (TOP): The highest rank of sergeant (except for the very specialized and rare Sergeant Major). Sometimes known as the "First Shirt." He runs the company.

FRAG: Army slang for what is essentially an act of murder. During the war, many NCO's and officers became so intent on gaining rank and glory that they would endanger their men. Fragging was nature's way of telling them they had made a mistake. It was usually accomplished by flipping a hand grenade (ours or theirs) into a room in which the subject was sleeping.

GREENIE: A new troop, one still wet behind the ears.

HAM CONNECTION: A way to communicate back to the world. Base commo could sometimes connect with a ham radio operator in Hawaii or elsewhere and patch together a bunch of such operators until they could get one close to your home. Then they'd patch into phone lines to reach a specific number. Unreliable, but a lot cheaper than trying the more direct overseas telephone system.

3

HUMPIN' THE BOONIES: Literally, packing a mass of equipment in the bush. Usually a reference to a long range patrol with full gear moving in the field.

IMPERIAL RUNNING DOG: Propagandist term used to describe almost anybody the ruling communists thought was against them.

IRON TRIANGLE: V.C. strongpoint just northwest of Saigon.

JOE: Traditional name Vietnamese called Americans they didn't know by name. Short for G.I. Joe (left over from WWII).

JUICE: Pull or influence. Also used to mean bribe money.

KLICKS: Slang for kilometers. The 'new' unit of measure.

KY: Premier of South Vietnam in 1966.

LZ: Landing Zone, where a chopper can set down to pick up or land troops.

MONSOON: Rainy season in most of Asia. In Vietnam, it generally runs from late May through September.

NAZIS: You all know this one — National Socialists, the guys who tried to conquer the world in WWII. After the war, many of them fled the war crime tribunals in Germany and slipped through Switzerland to Africa where a great number were enlisted into the French Foreign Legion. They ended up fighting the Vietminh.

NUMBAH ONE (or TEN): Vietnamese/American slang for something very good (NUMBAH ONE) or something very bad (NUMBAH TEN).

NVN: The (regular) North Vietnamese Army.

'155: Armyese for a 155 Millimeter howitzer. A long range piece of artillery. The '155 could lob a shell in a high arc for a considerable distance, although the shells moved relatively slowly. Good for long range cover from a safe area.

PACIFIED: A village or area that was on "our" side. Or one that was full of dead people.

PURPLE HEART: Decoration given to troops wounded in a combat zone.

REMF: A *very* rude, crude way of describing military gentlemen who stayed behind the lines and never ever entered the field.

RE-UP: Re-enlist. Sign up for another period of time in the military.

RT: Radio Telephone.

SACK: Also "sack out," "catch some z's," etc. Get some sleep.

SHORT: Running out of time on an enlistment or tour of duty. Getting ready to get out and go home.

SLICKY-BOY: A hustler, con man, or some Asian trying to make a quick buck.

SUCKING CHEST WOUND: A wound that penetrates the lung causing air to flow into the chest, deflating the lung. Very serious and often deadly.

TUNNEL RUNNERS: Later, tunnel rats. Troops picked and trained especially to fight in the tunnels.

THE 25th: The 25th Infantry, parent group to the 23rd.

UNCLE HO: Ho Chi Minh, spiritual and temporal leader of the VC.

VIETMINH: Forerunner of the VC. Freedom fighters against the French until the end at Dienbienphu.

WILLY PETER: White Phosphorus. Usually loaded into grenades or shells. It will burn with any exposure to oxygen, even the oxygen in water. Very scary stuff.

XIN LOI: Another Vietnamese phrase, used as an apology.

U.S. ARMY CRIMINAL
INVESTIGATION COMMAND

PURPLE
HEART

MARVEL®

75¢ US
95¢ CAN

5 APR

CC 02435

APPROVED
BY THE
COMICS
CODE
AUTHORITY

THOMAS...!

WHAT TH...!

CRIPES, THOMAS! WHAT ARE YOU THINKING OF!?

8

INJURY IN A *COMBAT ZONE*, AND ALL THAT.

AND WHO MIGHT *THIS* BE, SGT. POLKOW? AND WHERE IS SPECIALIST LITTLE?

THIS IS SPECIALIST *HALE*, YOUR NEW CLERK. HE'S A FULLY QUALIFIED CLERK-TYPIST. DOESN'T HAVE TO LOOK AT THE KEYS ...

SO. A *REAL* CLERK TYPIST. BUT *WHERE* IS SPECIALIST LITTLE?

SERGEANT LITTLE NOW. HE'S IN THE FIELD, WHERE HE BELONGS, WITH A SQUAD FROM MY PLATOON.

YOU SENT *MY* CLERK INTO THE *FIELD*? BEHIND MY BACK?

IF YOU DON'T LIKE IT, TALK TO LT. FINELLI! HE OK'ED IT. IF YOU WANT TO TALK TO ME, YOU KNOW WHERE TO FIND ME!

SLAM

A REAL CLERK-TYPIST, EH? COME, MY BOY--LET'S REPAIR TO THE CLUB AND DISCUSS MY POLICIES FOR THE COMPANY.

JUST A COUPLE MORE MINUTES.

CHEZ G.I. I ALWAYS LOVED FRANKS AND BEANS.

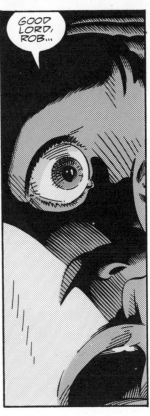

11

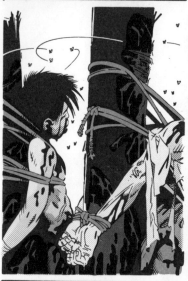

IT SHALL BE AS I SAY, SGT. POLKOW! UPON HIS RETURN, *SGT.* LITTLE WILL RETURN TO THE ORDERLY ROOM. NOW OFF WITH YOU, I'M EXPECTING SOME NEW REPLACEMENTS ANY TIME.

SLAM

ORDERLY ROOM

HEADQUART
4/23
INFAN
(MECHANIZ

WHO THE HECK WAS THAT? HE LOOKED *MEAN!*

EITHER MEAN OR *ANGRY!* I DON'T THINK I'D LIKE HIM TO BE ANGRY WITH ME!

HEY, MAN, DON'T MEAN A THING. THE BIGGER THEY ARE, THE BIGGER THEY ARE, YOU KNOW?

SO GENTLEMEN, WELCOME TO THE 23RD INFANTRY. WE AIM TO PLEASE, HERE. IS THERE ANYTHING *SPECIAL* ANY OF YOU REQUIRE IN YOUR DUTY ASSIGNMENTS?

I AIN'T NO GREENIE, MAN. AND I DON'T PAY OFF NO *REMF* FIRST SERGEANTS!

13

AS YOU WISH. HALE, PLEASE SEE TO IT THAT THESE MEN GET TO SGT. POLKOW. HE NEEDS SOME REPLACEMENTS AND I'M SURE THEY'LL ENJOY LIFE WITH HIM.

NO WAY AROUND IT. WE'VE GOT TO CROSS!

ROB, THIS SHOULD DO IT!

AS MIKE WOULD SAY: A LITTLE *DET CORD*, AND VOILA! INSTANT BRIDGE!

HELP!

THOMAS, YOU IDIOT!

A SHORT TIME LATER...

THOMAS, I'VE HEARD ALL KINDS OF STORIES ABOUT YOU, BUT I NEVER COULD BELIEVE THEM. UNTIL *NOW*!

QUIET! COMPANY'S COMING! ROB...

16

SOMETIME LATER... YOU'D **BETTER** GET IT TO WORK, THOMAS, OR I'M GOING TO SEND YOU DOWN THERE BARE-NAKED AS A DIVERSION!

NEVER SAW THEM SO **CARELESS** BEFORE.

THEY'RE ONLY HUMAN, ED, AND THEY FEEL **SAFE**.

GREEN TWIG TWO TO OVERDOG. GREEN TWIG TWO TO OVERDOG. COME IN OVERDOG.

IF HE DOESN'T GET IT WORKING SOON, WE'LL HAVE TO PULL BACK. WE CAN'T TAKE THIS MANY ALONE.

I'D HATE TO LET THEM GET AWAY...

GOT 'EM, ROB. GOOD CONTACT WITH A '155 OUTFIT. ALREADY KNEW THEIR FREEK AND THEY'RE ONLY ABOUT TEN KLICKS OUT.

THAT'LL SAVE SOME RED TAPE BULL, WHAT'S THEIR **CALL SIGN?**

REDSHIRT TWELVE.

REDSHIRT 12, THIS IS GREENTWIG 2. GOT A SPECIAL FIRE MISSION FOR YA!

17

AND, SOME DISTANCE AWAY...

...SOME PATROL NEEDS FIRE QUICK! WHAT THE HEY, WE CAN SPARE AMMO. GET IT GOING!

GREAT SHOT! THAT WAS DEAD CENTER! FIRE FOR EFFECT!

I JUST HEARD THAT YOU TURNED DOWN LITTLE'S CALL FOR AN EXTRACTION! THEY MUST BE LOW ON FOOD AND AMMO! **WHAT** ARE YOU TRYING TO DO?

JUST MY JOB, SGT. POLKOW. IT IS MY **DUTY** TO SEE THE AMERICAN TAXPAYER'S MONEY IS NOT WASTED. YOUR PEOPLE CAN FIND THEIR WAY BACK WITHOUT SPENDING THOUSANDS OF DOLLARS ON A HELICOPTER. AFTER ALL, WE **ARE** THE INFANTRY!

ALL RIGHT, TOP. HAVE IT YOUR WAY. FOR NOW!

TAKE OVER, HALE. I'M GOING TO THE CLUB FOR A LITTLE BRACER!

RAMNARAIN! JUST THE MAN I WANTED TO SEE. I WANT YOU TO DO SOMETHING FOR ME!

23

POUR IT IN! POUND THOSE SUCKERS!

THE ALTAR BOY SPEAKS AGAIN. I DON'T KNOW IF MY LILY-WHITE EARS CAN TAKE IT!

GUESS THE CONVOY HAD A LITTLE MORE JUICE THAN WE DID!

AND IT LOOKS LIKE CHARLIE HAS LOST HIS!

LATER, THE ROAD CLEARED.

THANKS A BUNCH, GUYS. FOR THE LIFT AND THE WORK-OUT.

C'MON. HURRY IT UP. MIKE'S DUE IN TODAY.

24

C'MON GUYS, MIKE'LL BE IN IN A COUPLE OF HOURS, DON'T GO TO SLEEP YET!

GO MEET HIM YOUR-SELF. I *GOTTA* GET SOME SACK.

I'LL COME WITH YOU, ED. JUST GIVE ME A MINUTE TO TELL POLKOW WE'RE BACK. MEET YOU IN THE *MESS HALL.*

JUST IN FROM THE BUSH, EH?

HOW CAN YOU TELL?

YOU KIDDIN', MAN. WE COULD *SMELL* YOU 20 KLICKS OUT!

I'M ED MARKS, 3RD PLATOON. I HAVEN'T SEEN YOU GUYS AROUND HERE BEFORE.

WE JUST GOT IN. I'M JOSE *SANTOS.* THIS HERE IS FITZ *MILLS* AND RALPH *MARCHESE.* THERE'S A GUY NAMED CHANDRADAT RAMNARAIN TOO, FROM SOME LITTLE INDIAN COLONY IN SOUTH AMERICA -- DON'T KNOW WHERE HE'S AT RIGHT NOW.

C'MON ED, WE GOTTA HUSTLE. POLKOW SAYS MIKE CAUGHT A CHOPPER AND SHOULD BE HERE IN A COUPLE OF *MINUTES.* THEN WE'VE GOT TO SEE TOP.

RIGHT! SEE YOU GUYS!

MUST BE HIM!

ROB! ED! DID YOU GUYS MISS ME? WHAT A *GREAT* TIME! I GOT A MILLION THINGS TO TELL YOU!

WHY WASTE MY TIME?

SOME RAIN, GUYS. IT'S HARDER THAN THE SHOWER.

YUP. BE LIKE THIS FOR A COUPLE OF MONTHS, EXCEPT WHEN IT RAINS HARDER!

WHA...!

CHECK THE REST OUT. BET YOU'VE GOT FUNGUS IN ALL THE SEAMS. IT'S ALL THE WATER.

YOU'RE RIGHT, MIKE.

THERE'S SOME KIND OF GREEN GUNK ALL AROUND THE SEAMS! WHAT CAN I DO ABOUT IT?

NOT MUCH. TRY SOME LYSOL OR SOMETHING. AND TRY TO GET THEM DRYED OUT ONCE IN A WHILE.

SURE, DRY THEM OUT! WHEN IT'S NOT RAINING, WE'RE OUT IN THE BOONIES SOMEWHERE WADING RIVERS. KEEP 'EM DRY. HUH!

YOU GUYS SEE THIS? KY WANTS *US* TO INVADE THE NORTH. SAYS IT'S THE ONLY WAY TO END THE WAR! HOW ABOUT THOSE APPLES?

NEVER HAPPEN, MAN. OLD LBJ'D...

33

I ALWAYS THOUGHT THE RED CROSS...

YOU HEARD WHAT THEY SAID. THEY'RE ONLY ALLOWED TO DO SOMETHING FOR A DIRECT RELATION, LIKE A MOTHER OR FATHER. THEY COULDN'T DO ANYTHING! COME ON NOW, DRINK UP.

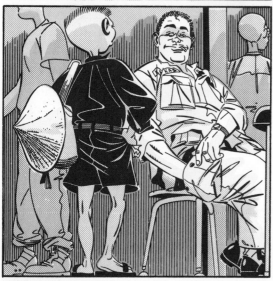

HELLO JOE! WANT SOME NUMBAH ONE SPECIAL SOUVENIERS?

WELL, WELL. THE J.C. PENNY OF CHU CHI! WHAT'S HAPPENING, NGUEN?

NGUEN'S THE LOCAL SLICKY-BOY. SELL YOU ANYTHING. WHERE HAVE YOU BEEN, NGUEN?

I VISIT FAMILY UP NORTH. FIND LOT OF GOOD SOUVENIERS. MANY VC KILLED THERE. LOOK! REAL CHARLIE HAT!

LOOKS LIKE A REAL, NVA HELMET. WHAT ELSE YOU GOT LIKE THAT, NGUEN?

LOTS OF STUFF. MORE AT HOME. GOT NUMBAH ONE CHARLIE GRENADES. SOLD ONE TO JOE BACK THERE--CAN GET MORE IF YOU'RE INTERESTED!

NOW WHY WOULD *HE*... OH, WELL, WE'D BETTER GET ED HERE BACK TO THE HOOCH. C'MON MIKE, FINISH UP AND LET'S GO.

THE NEXT DAY...

YOU'LL HAVE TO TAKE 'EM OUT, ROB. I CAN'T HOLD MY PIECE RIGHT YET, AND THIS PAUL REVERE THING STILL ISN'T OVER WITH. BE CAREFUL. FOR MY SAKE.

LATER...

IT *WAS* A COMMIE GRENADE.

YEAH, AND NGUEN SAID HE SOLD ONE TO HIM.

LOOK AT THE LITTLE...

IF I EVER TAKE ANOTHER DRINK...

38

GUERILLAS! HERE? THIS IS JUST A PEACEFUL VILLAGE.

I AM GLAD IT IS SO PEACEFUL. WE WILL NOT DISTURB YOU, BUT SURELY YOU WON'T MIND IF WE WALK THROUGH AND AVOID THE MUD OF THE FIELDS?

WE WOULD BE PROUD TO HAVE OUR AMERICAN FRIENDS VISIT. JUST FOLLOW THIS DIKE FOR ANOTHER TWO OR THREE KLICKS. WE WILL GO AHEAD TO PREPARE A WELCOME.

AREN'T YOU WORRIED ABOUT WHAT KIND OF RECEPTION THEY'LL SET UP FOR US, ROB?

A HOT ONE, I'M SURE, SARGE. I SPEAK THE LANGUAGE. THOSE BOYS WERE VC AND THEY'LL BE LOOKING FOR US.

OF COURSE THEY'RE CHARLIE. THEY CAME BECAUSE OF THAT MESSENGER THE LAST VILLAGE SENT OUT. BUT THEY'LL BE WAITING FOR US UP AHEAD, WON'T THEY?

LATER...

YUP, JUST AS I THOUGHT!

THEY THINK WE'RE WITH THEIR FRIENDS. LET'S LET THEM KNOW THEY MADE A MISTAKE! JERRY, MAKE SURE WE GET THE OXEN. ED, THOSE HUTS AT THE EDGE OF THE VILLAGE ARE WHERE THE SUPPLIES ARE. GET THE REST OF THE SQUAD UP HERE.

KAKAS! PASS THE WORD, GET KAKAS UP HERE!

STAY HERE, AL. I WANT YOU WHERE I CAN SEE YOU ALL THE TIME. NEVER KNOW WHAT SORT OF MISCHIEF YOU MIGHT GET IN OTHERWISE.

42

45

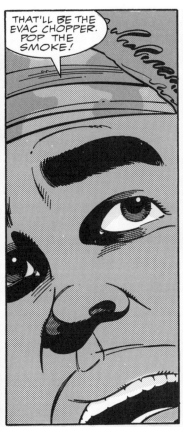

THAT'LL BE THE EVAC CHOPPER. POP THE SMOKE!

RIGHT, RED SMOKE!

INCOMING!

COME ON! MOVE IT!! WE'VE GOT TO GET OUT OF HERE!

ISN'T ANY-
ONE FLYING
COVER FOR
THIS THING?

COME ON! GET THE LEAD OUT! LET'S GET THE HECK OUT OF HERE!

MARVEL®

THE 'NAM

5¢ US
95¢ CAN
7
JUNE
© 02435

APPROVED
BY THE
COMICS
CODE
AUTHORITY

GOOD OLD DAYS

STORY: **DOUG MURRAY** PENCILS pp.1 and 22: **MICHAEL GOLDEN** INKS pp.1 and 22: **BOB McLEOD**
ALL OTHER ART: **WAYNE VANSANT** LETTERING: **KURT HATHAWAY** COLORING: **PHIL FELIX**
EDITOR: **LARRY HAMA** EDITOR-IN-CHIEF: **JIM SHOOTER**

STAN LEE PRESENTS:

AN LZ SOMEWHERE IN THE IRON TRIANGLE...

THE 'NAM

OK, MEN. BASE SAYS ABOUT AN HOUR. REST UP AND SMOKE 'EM IF YOU GOT 'EM.

HI, DUONG, HOW'S IT GOING?

DUONG, DO YOU MIND IF I ASK YOU A QUESTION?

YES?

YOU'RE A KIT CARSON SCOUT, RIGHT? THAT MEANS YOU USED TO BE V.C. WHY? WHY DID YOU CHANGE?

A TALL ORDER! WELL, IT ALL BEGAN...

1940. THE JAPANESE SWING DOWN FROM CHINA TO CONQUER ALL OF ASIA.

I GUESS IT ALL STARTED WHEN THE JAPANESE INVADED...

The elements of this story are completely true. Duong's story is actually a composite of the stories of three different VC--not all of whom changed sides and became Kit Carson Scouts. By using these stories, I think we've given a clear picture of the roots of the war--the reason Charlie fought as long and hard as he did.

The artwork was done by Wayne Vansant, a new artist with a special interest in--and aptitude for--work about the French Foreign Legion. By letting Wayne do this special issue, we've given Michael Golden some extra time to do some really special work on future issues of THE NAM. Michael will be back next issue.

Doug Murray

"THE FRENCH REACTED AS THEY HAD IN EUROPE. THEY COOPERATED."

"BUT NOT EVERYONE DID. MY, WIFE, FOR INSTANCE."

"WHEN THEY KILLED HER, SOMETHING WITHIN ME CHANGED. I WAS NO LONGER A SIMPLE FARMER."

"I WENT TO COLLEGE AT THE LYCEE ALBERT SARRAUT, IN HANOI."

"AND MET PHAN BOI CHAU, A NATIONALIST TEACHER WHO WAS UNDER HOUSE ARREST FOR TELLING US WE SHOULD HAVE OUR FREEDOM."

"EVENTUALLY I GRADUATED."

"AND BEGAN MY REAL WORK. FREEING MY COUNTRY."

"I BECAME A MEMBER OF THE VIETMINH."

"AND LEARNED TO KILL."

"BUT I NEVER FORGOT MY DREAM-- THE DREAM OF MY WIFE! A FREE VIETNAM!"

"FINALLY THE END CAME."

"THE JAPANESE WERE GONE AND UNCLE HO SPOKE OF *ALL MEN BEING CREATED EQUAL.*"

"WE MARCHED ON THE DISTRICT HEADQUARTERS."

"AND OUR LEADER TOOK COMMAND. FOR THE PEOPLE!"

"EVEN THEN, THOUGH..."

"SOMETHING WAS WRONG."

"TIME PASSED..."

"I WAS NOT POLITICAL."

"AGAIN I BECAME A SIMPLE FARMER."

"AND I AGAIN FOUND SOMEONE SPECIAL TO ME."

"AND BEGAN TO MAKE A NEW LIFE."

"THEN, IN 1954, IT ALL CAME APART AGAIN. THE FRENCH SEEMED DETERMINED TO KEEP US THEIR COLONY... THEIR SERVANTS. THE REST OF THE WORLD SEEMED UNINTERESTED."

⑥

"WAR HAD COME ONCE AGAIN."

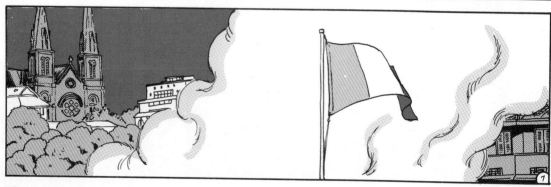

"I BECAME A SQUAD LEADER, THAN A TROOP COMMANDER."

"AND I FOUGHT THE FRENCH!"

"THEN THE FRENCH BROUGHT IN SPECIAL TROOPS!"

13e DEMI-BRIGADE de LÉGION ÉTRANGÈRE

"THE WAR WAS BARELY OVER AND THEY HAD NAZIS WORKING FOR THEM! NAZIS!"

⑧

"WE TRIED EVERYTHING AGAINST THEM."

"BUT THEY WERE FORMIDABLE FIGHTERS."

"AND ALWAYS, THEY HAD BETTER WEAPONS AND EQUIPMENT."

"EVENTUALLY, I WAS WOUNDED AND WENT HOME TO RECOVER."

"BUT THIS WAS WAR!"

SHE WILL DIE IF YOU DON'T TALK!

"AND WAR HAS NO PITY, NO MERCY!"

SUBHUMAN PIG!

"NO MERCY AT ALL!"

"AND I DECIDED SOMETHING."

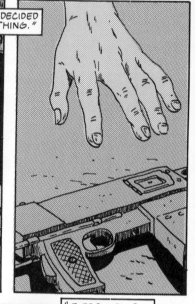

"LIKE WAR..."

"I TOO WOULD HAVE NO MERCY!"

"FINALLY, AT DIENBIENPHU, THE WAR WAS OVER."

"WE HAD WON OUR FREEDOM."

12

"BUT THAT WASN'T THE END OF IT."

"THE DIPLOMATS TALKED, AND MY COUNTRY STILL WASN'T FREE."

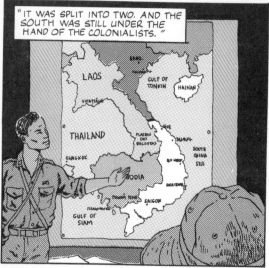

"IT WAS SPLIT INTO TWO. AND THE SOUTH WAS STILL UNDER THE HAND OF THE COLONIALISTS."

"THERE WAS STILL WORK TO DO."

"SUDDENLY, THERE WAS AN ELECTION."

HỒNG-LAN

"THE IMPERIAL RUNNING DOG WAS PREMIERE!"

NH DIỆM
ONG
HÂN TRĂM SỐ PHIẾU

"AND HIS TROOPS WERE AS BAD AS THE FRENCH."

"AND THEY WERE TRYING TO DESTROY ANY OPPOSITION!"

"BUT THEY DID NOT SUCCEED."

14

"BUT THERE SEEMED NO JUSTICE ANYWHERE."

"EVEN MY OWN COMRADES WERE OPPRESSING THE PEOPLE, INSTITUTING 'CLASSES' BASED ON BACKGROUND!"

SOMEHOW, THOSE WHO HAD BEEN POOR WERE BETTER THAN THOSE WITH EDUCATION OR PARENTS WHO HAD BEEN LANDOWNERS."

"IT DIDN'T LOOK LIKE FREEDOM TO ME."

"THEN THE AMERICANS CAME."

"THEY BEGAN TO BUILD GREAT BASES... "

"WHERE THEY COULD FEEL SECURE."

"THEN THEY WENT INTO OUR CITIES. "

"AND TRIED TO BUY EVERYTHING!"

"BUT THEY WERE NEVER REALLY SECURE. "

"NOT IN THEIR BASES..."

"NOT IN OUR CITIES. "

"THEY WERE NEVER SAFE. "

"BUT THE AMERICANS GOT BETTER."

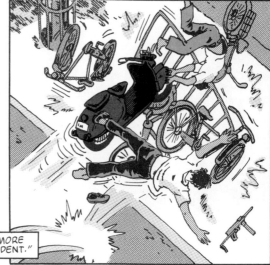

"AND MORE CONFIDENT."

"MEANWHILE, I KEPT FIGHTING."

18

"BUT IT WAS NOT THE SAME."

"YOU AMERICANS WANTED TO HELP."

"WHILE MY PEOPLE..."

"I DO NOT KNOW WHAT MY PEOPLE WERE TRYING TO DO!"

"AS TIME PASSED..."

"I BECAME MORE AND MORE UNSURE..."

"THAT I WAS ON THE RIGHT SIDE."

FINALLY...

"I MADE MY DECISION."

HOME OF THE
4/23 INFANTRY
MECHIVIZED OF COURSE
TROPIC LIGHTNING

"I CAME TO YOUR PEOPLE..."

"WHERE I HAVE BEEN ACCEPTED."

73

MARVEL®
© 1987 MARVEL ENTERTAINMENT GROUP, INC.

75¢ US
95¢ CAN
8
JULY

APPROVED
BY THE
COMICS
CODE
AUTHORITY

02435

Stan Lee presents: THE 'NAM

DOUG MURRAY — WRITER
MICHAEL GOLDEN — PENCILER
JOHN BEATTY — INKER
PHIL FELIX — LETTERS/COLOR
LARRY HAMA — EDITOR
JIM SHOOTER — EDITOR IN CHIEF

"IN THE UNDERGROUND"

SOMEWHERE NEAR CHU CHI. AUGUST 12, 1966.

OK MEN, TAKE FIVE. SMOKE 'EM IF YOU GOT 'EM!

LOOK AT THIS, MAN. NOT 20 KLICKS FROM THE 25TH'S FRONT DOOR. WHAT DO THEY EXPECT TO FIND HERE?

OURS NOT TO REASON WHY ...

DON'T MOVE, ED. JUST DON'T MOVE A MUSCLE.

WHA...

75

I THINK THIS IS WHAT WE'VE BEEN LOOKING FOR! LIEUTENANT!

MARKS, ALBERGO--MAKE SURE NOTHING POPS OUT OF THAT! THOMAS, BRING THE RADIO OVER HERE.

LOOKS GOOD, LIEUTENANT! THIS WAS PROBABLY MINED TO PREVENT OUR UN-COVERING IT. LT. ESPINO, LET'S GET YOUR TUNNEL RUNNERS IN THERE ASAP.

LOOKS LIKE A GOOD ONE!

OK MARTY, GET ON DOWN AND I'LL FOLLOW RIGHT BE-HIND. BE CAREFUL!

AIEEE!

YOU MEN, PUT A FRAG DOWN HERE! HURRY!

MEDIC!

THAT SHOULD TAKE CARE OF THAT!

I DON'T THINK I LIKE THE LOOKS OF THAT!

I DEFINITEY DON'T LIKE THE LOOKS OF THAT!

LISTEN UP...

THEY NEED SOMEONE ELSE TO GO DOWN INTO THE TUNNEL, TO HELP THE TUNNEL RUNNER WITH COMMUNICATIONS. THEY WANT A VOLUNTEER.

SURE, A VOLUNTEER! LISTEN, I'D LOVE TO HELP, BUT I'VE GOT THIS PROBLEM...

DON'T WORRY ABOUT IT, MIKE. I'LL DO IT.

CAREFUL, HERE. COME SLOWLY, AND STAY DOWN.

WATCH THIS!

THIS'S A BAMBOO SNAKE. VERY DEADLY.

CHARLIE LEAVES 'EM OUT HERE SO WE BRUSH 'EM OFF AND THEY BRUSH US OFF.

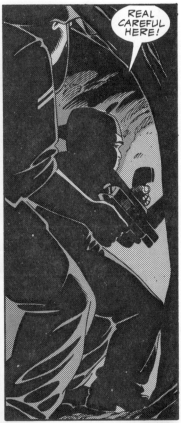

SEE THAT!

SHE'S THEIR LAST DITCH BOOBY-TRAP. THEY'RE ALL GONE BY NOW.

YOU MEAN...

YOU GOT IT, MAN! THAT WAS DELIBERATE!

NOTHING MORE WE'RE GONNA FIND--

--LET'S SEE IF THAT'S A WAY OUT!

AMERICAN! I'M AN AMERICAN! APPLE PIE, THE WORLD SERIES, OH, SAY CAN YOU SEE!

DON'T SHOOT!

LATER...

YOU DO THIS FOR A LIVING?

YEAH. NOT FOR LONG THOUGH. I'M GETTIN' SHORT. GONNA RE-UP AND GO AIRBORNE. GET SOME EXTRA MONEY AND GET OUT OF THE MUD.

WON'T DO ANY GOOD. THERE'S TUNNELS ALL AROUND HERE. ALL OVER THE PLACE.

ALL RIGHT MEN, LET'S MOVE OUT AND GO HOME.

5th TO THE 1st: by Doug Murray & Mike Golden

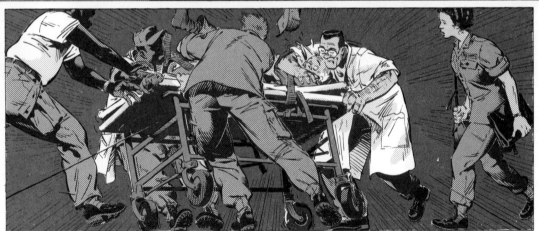

the TUNNEL RAT

YOU EVER NOTICE HOW **SOUNDS** KIND OF STAY WITH YOU? I MEAN, WHEN I WAS A KID WATCHING ALL THOSE DUKE WAYNE FILMS ON TV, ALL THE GUNS MADE THESE LOUD EXPLOSIVE NOISES WHEN THEY WENT OFF. WHEN I GOT HERE, I FOUND THAT THE LOUDEST NOISE WAS THE SOUND OF METAL AGAINST METAL AS THE BOLT RUNS BACK AND FORTH. ANOTHER SOUND I WON'T FORGET IS THE BUZZ OF THE **VULCAN**.

THE VULCAN WAS THIS NEW WEAPON WE GOT STUCK PLAYING NURSEMAID FOR. SEEMS THE ARMY HAD COME UP WITH A NEW WRINKLE ON THE OLD GATLING GUN--THIS ONE WAS ELECTRIC AND FIRED GOD-KNOWS-HOW-MANY ROUNDS A MINUTE. ALL WE COULD HEAR WAS A LOUD SORT OF **BUZZ** AS THE ROUNDS CAME OUT--AND SEE A RIVER OF BRASS FLOWING FROM THE VENT OF THIS MODIFIED **APC** THE THING WAS MOUNTED IN.

INTELLIGENCE HAD COME UP WITH LOCATIONS ON THREE VILLAGES THAT CHARLIE WAS USING FOR SUPPLY AND REST POINTS. THE VULCAN (WITH US AS INFANTRY COVER) WAS SUPPOSED TO TEACH THE VILLAGERS THE HAZARDS OF MESSING AROUND WITH UNCLE SUGAR.

NATURALLY, AS WE WERE THE GOOD GUYS, WE DROPPED LEAFLETS TO WARN THE PEOPLE THAT WE WERE COMING-- JUST AS NATURALLY, WHEN WE ARRIVED, THE VILLAGE WAS COMPLETELY **DESERTED.** THE VULCAN OPENED UP ANYWAY, AND WHEN THE DUST CLEARED, THE VILLAGE WAS GONE--JUST A PILE OF DEBRIS WITH DIRT SETTLING OVER IT.

WE MOVED IN TO CHECK IT OUT AND ONE OF OUR ALERT FLANKERS (GOOD OL' 'FATS' DUFF) FOUND SOMETHING IMPORTANT. HE FELL THROUGH AN ENTRANCE HATCH INTO WHAT WAS EVIDENTLY A SERIES OF **TUNNELS.**

WE'D SEEN **VC** TUNNELS BEFORE-- A BUNCH HAD BEEN AROUND DA NANG COMPLETE WITH UNDERGROUND HOSPITALS, LIVING QUARTERS, MAP ROOMS--THE WHOLE MAGILLA. THE FACT THAT DUFF HADN'T BEEN SHOT OR KNIFED WHEN HE FELL IN MADE ME FAIRLY SURE THIS ONE WAS DESERTED--AND THE FACT THAT WE HAD TWO MORE VILLAGES TO EDUCATE BEFORE NIGHTFALL MADE ME VERY SURE I COULDN'T STAY TO CHECK IT OUT. I CALLED FOR A **BACKUP** AND LEFT TWO OF MY BOYS (FATS AS THE DISCOVERER AND 'FUDD' VERZYL) TO KEEP AN EYE ON THINGS.

SP5 FRANK VERZYL HAD WORKED AS A TUNNEL RAT AROUND DA NANG BEFORE BEING ASSIGNED TO MY PLATOON. TUNNEL RATS WERE MADMEN WHO WENT DOWN INTO THESE HOLES, USUALLY WITH JUST A HANDGUN OR SHOTGUN, AND SWEPT THEM CLEAN OF VC SO INTELLIGENCE COULD CHECK THEM OUT IN PERFECT SAFETY (SOMETHING THAT WAS VERY IMPORTANT TO INTELLIGENCE).

TUNNEL RATS WERE DARING, RESOURCEFUL AND USUALLY SURVIVED FOR ABOUT THREE WEEKS. VERZYL HAD BEATEN THE ODDS, AND ACQUIRED THE NICKNAME OF 'FUDD' BECAUSE HE LOVED HUNTING THOSE 'WASCALLY WABBITS' IN THE TUNNELS. I KNEW THAT, BUT I LEFT HIM THERE ANYWAY.

I GOT THE REST OF THE STORY SECOND-HAND FROM FATS. SEEMS AS SOON AS WE GOT OUT OF SIGHT, FUDD HAD PULLED OFF HIS RUCKSACK AND CLIMBED DOWN INTO THE TUNNEL FOR A LOOK AROUND. DUFF HADN'T PROTESTED, HE WAS BUSY PULLIN' AN EYELID INSPECTION AND AFTER ALL, FUDD WAS EXPERIENCED AND THE COMPLEX EMPTY.

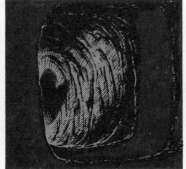

NEAR AS I CAN FIGURE, FUDD TRAMPED AROUND IN THE TUNNELS FOR ABOUT A HALF-HOUR WITHOUT FINDING ANY-THING. FINALLY, HE CAME UPON A CLOSED DOOR NEAR THE BACK END OF THE COMPLEX--ONE HE HEARD **NOISES** BEHIND. HE FIGURED HE'D FOUND A MAP ROOM OR A FILE CENTER, POSSIBLY WITH A VC OFFICER STILL IN IT, SO HE COCKED HIS HANDGUN, KICKED OPEN THE DOOR AND TOOK A LOOK.

HE WASN'T READY FOR WHAT HE SAW.

SEEMS THE VC HAD LEFT IN A HURRY--THIS ROOM HAD BEEN THEIR LARDER, IT HAD HAD SOME FOOD LEFT IN IT, AND THE ATTENDANT **RATS.** THE RATS HAD BEEN WITHOUT FOOD FOR DAYS, MAYBE WEEKS, AND THEY'D BEEN TRAPPED. WHEN FUDD OPENED UP, HE FOUND HIMSELF ACTING AS A RED CARPET FOR A COUPLE DOZEN BIG, HUNGRY RATS. I SHUDDER WHEN I THINK ABOUT IT. ANYWAY, FUDD BROKE AND HEADED TOPSIDE AS FAST AS HE COULD. BROKE SURFACE A COUPLE OF YARDS FROM DUFF, SCARING THE CRUD OUT OF HIM.

AFTER A COUPLE OF MINUTES OF SHAKING AND SOBBING, FUDD STARTED TO PULL HIMSELF TOGETHER--BEGAN TO TELL DUFF THE STORY IN BITS AND PIECES. HE WAS ALMOST BACK TO NORMAL WHEN THE **BACKUP** I'D CALLED ARRIVED. THE OFFICER IN CHARGE WAS A GREENIE--A BRAND NEW 2ND LOOIE RIGHT OUT OF **OCS**, AND HE WANTED TO KNOW RIGHT **NOW** WHAT WAS IN THOSE TUNNELS. FUDD STARTED SWEATING AS HE TRIED TO TELL THE LT. WHAT HE'D FOUND, BUT HE COULDN'T HAVE BEEN TOO COHERENT, AND THE LT. WASN'T TOO PATIENT. HE WANTED TO GO DOWN AND SEE FOR HIMSELF, AND HE WANTED FUDD AS A GUIDE.

FUDD REALLY STARTED SHAKING THEN AND ASKED, HECK, ACCORDING TO DUFF, HE **BEGGED** THE LT. NOT TO MAKE HIM GO BACK DOWN. BUT LIKE I SAID, THIS GUY WAS A GREENIE, HE ORDERED FUDD TO GO, AND SAID HE'D ARREST HIM IF HE DIDN'T.

FUDD DID THE ONLY THING HE COULD THINK OF--HE PULLED HIS SIDEARM AND SHOT THE LT. ON THE SPOT.

I SAW FUDD TWICE MORE. AT THE COURT MARTIAL, WHICH WAS REAL SHORT-- FUDD WAS A RAVING **MADMAN** WHEN THEY BROUGHT HIM IN AND IT DIDN'T TAKE SIGMUND FREUD TO REALIZE THAT HE WAS SERIOUSLY CRAZY.

AND WHEN THEY TOOK HIM TO HIS PLANE--HE WAS STRAPPED TO A HOSPITAL GURNEY, COULD BARELY MOVE, BUT WHEN THE **C130** ROLLED UP AND THE REAR END OPENED, IT LOOKED LIKE THE BIGGEST, BLACKEST **TUNNEL** MOUTH YOU'VE EVER SEEN, HE NEARLY BROKE FREE. IT TOOK FOUR CORPSMEN TO GET HIM ABOARD AND HE WAS **SCREAMING** SOMETHING AWFUL.

I STILL HEAR THAT SCREAMING SOMETIMES IN MY HEAD-- LIKE I SAID, THE **SOUNDS** KIND OF STAY WITH YOU.